chatterbox

ACTIVITY BOOK 4

Derek Strange and J. A. Holderness

My name is

_____

This is my book.

I started it on

_____ .

I finished it on

_____ .

Oxford University Press

Oxford University Press
Walton Street, Oxford OX2 6DP

Oxford New York
Athens Auckland Bangkok Bombay
Calcutta Cape Town Dar es Salaam Delhi
Florence Hong Kong Istanbul Karachi
Kuala Lumpur Madras Madrid Melbourne
Mexico City Nairobi Paris Singapore
Taipei Tokyo Toronto

and associated companies in
Berlin Ibadan

OXFORD and OXFORD ENGLISH are
trade marks of Oxford University Press

ISBN 0 19 432444 3

First published 1991
Sixth impression 1995

Illustrated by Judy Brown, Willow and Raymond Turvey
Photographs by Rob Judges
Pyramid photograph p. 62 by permission of
Spectrum Colour Library

Typeset by Pentacor PLC, High Wycombe, Bucks
Printed in Hong Kong

① Read and match. Write the name.

1. She made a list and then she went shopping with her basket. Who was it? _____

2. He stole Uncle John's magic book because he wanted to learn some magic. Who was it? _____

3. He ate all the chocolate cake – there was no cake for Uncle John. Who was it? _____

4. She pressed the wrong button on the Time Machine and it disappeared. Who was it? _____

5. He said a magic spell and changed the dinosaur back into bones again. Who was it? _____

6. She said a magic spell and they found Barker in a cupboard. Who was it? _____

② What are they dreaming about? Write the answers.

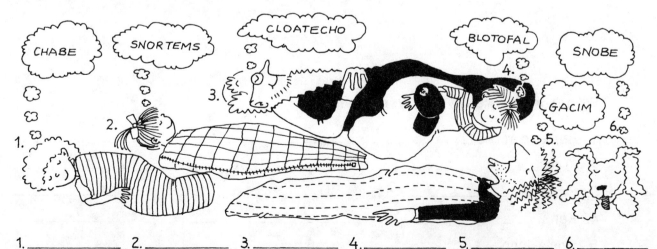

1._____ 2._____ 3._____ 4._____ 5._____ 6._____

③   **Read the story in your Pupil's Book again.**

Answer: right (√) or wrong (×)?

1. The book of Adabra is a very old book of magic spells. .... √ ×

2. Uncle John thinks the Book of Adabra is on Mars. .... √ ×

3. Some robots on Mars have got Uncle John's crystal ball. .... √ ×

4. Caroline can see a calendar inside the crystal ball. .... √ ×

5. The Time Machine arrives on Mars in the year 2060. .... √ ×

④   **Match the pictures.   Then write sentences.**

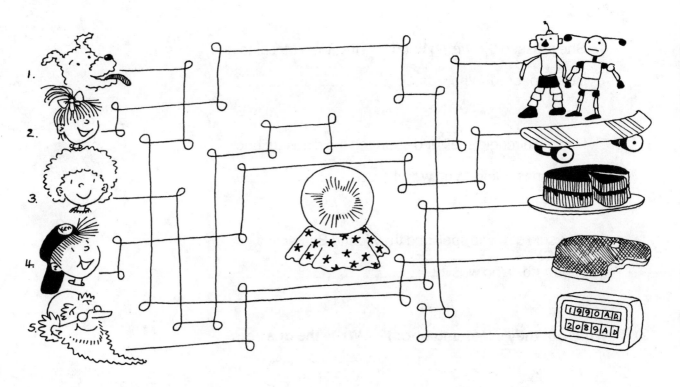

What can they see in the crystal ball?

1. Barker can see _____ .

2. Kate _____ .

3. Caroline _____ .

4. Ken _____ .

5. Uncle John _____ .

⑤   **Read this part of the story carefully.   Some things are missing.**
Write the story again and put in the missing things.

Why are we going to Mars asked Ken
Well Uncle John said Yesterday I looked in my
crystal ball . . . and I saw a robot magician
Did he have a magic wand asked Kate
No laughed Uncle John but his tricks were
very clever

'Why are we going to Mars?' asked Ken.
_____
_____
_____
_____
_____

⑥   **Read and match the dates and the calendars.**

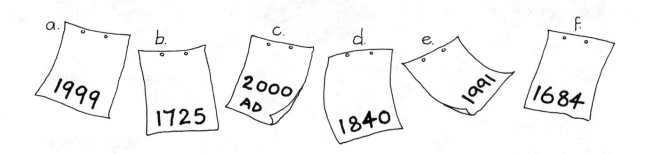

a. 1999
b. 1725
c. 2000 AD
d. 1840
e. 1991
f. 1684

1. nineteen hundred and ninety-one   **e**
2. two thousand   ☐
3. seventeen hundred and twenty-five   ☐
4. sixteen hundred and eighty-four   ☐
5. eighteen hundred and forty   ☐
6. nineteen hundred and ninety-nine   ☐

⑦ **Complete the crossword.**

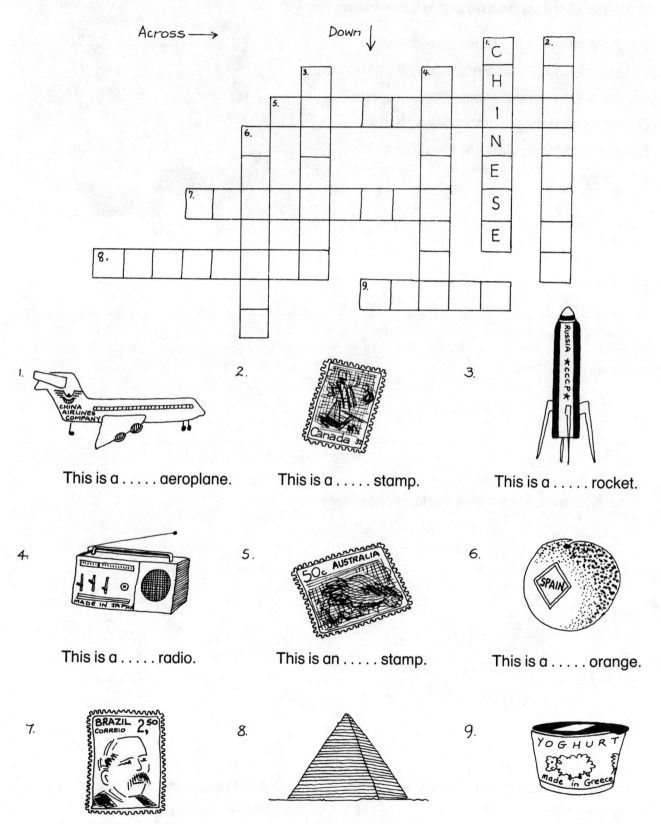

Across —→

Down ↓

1. This is a . . . . . aeroplane.

2. This is a . . . . . stamp.

3. This is a . . . . . rocket.

4. This is a . . . . . radio.

5. This is an . . . . . stamp.

6. This is a . . . . . orange.

7. This is a . . . . . stamp.

8. This is an . . . . . pyramid.

9. This is a . . . . . yoghurt.

① **Look at the picture.   Then write the words in the right boxes.**

wood	glass	paper	plastic	metal
	1. bottles			

② **Answer the questions.**

1. What are the bottles made of? _They're made of glass._

2. What is the spoon made of? _____

3. What is the book made of? _____

4. What are the scissors made of? _____

5. What are the records made of? _____

6. What is the box made of? _____

7. What are the supermarket bags made of? _____

③   **Read the story in your Pupil's Book again.**

     Answer: right (✓) or wrong (×)?

     1. Magixo was made of metal and glass. .... ✓ ×

     2. Magixo made two robot rabbits. .... ✓ ×

     3. Magixo was happy to see Uncle John and the children on Mars. .... ✓ ×

     4. Uncle John wanted to help Magixo. .... ✓ ×

     5. Magixo showed the Book of Adabra to Uncle John and the children. .... ✓ ×

④   **What is it?   Read and answer.**

     1. It is small. It is usually made of plastic and metal.

         You usually write postcards or letters with it. What is it? _____

     2. You buy them in a small box. They are usually brown.

         They are made of sugar and cocoa. What are they? _____

     3. Some of it is made of paper and some of it is made of metal.

         You buy things with it in shops. What is it? _____

     4. It is made of milk and sugar. Sometimes you put fruit in it too.

         You drink it. What is it? _____

     5. They are made of paper. They usually have pictures or

         photographs on them. You send them to your friends when

         you are on holiday. What are they? _____

⑤　**What do they need?　Complete the sentences.**

1.　　She needs some water. _____

2. _____

3. _____

4. _____

5. _____

⑥　**What are they saying?　Read.　Then write in the cartoon.**

'What's this?' asked Caroline. 'It's not moving. It's made of metal and glass . . . It's a statue.'

'No,' said Ken. 'It's a machine . . . . a robot!'

'Good evening, Earth People,' the robot said. 'My name is Magixo.'

'Magixo?' said Uncle John. 'Are you a magician?'

What's this? It's not moving.
_____

No, _____
_____

⑦ **Read and match.**

1. Why is it difficult to eat
   inside the space shuttle? . . .

2. Why do astronauts have TV
   cameras inside space shuttles? . . .

3. Why are chocolates brown? . . .

4. Why can't penguins fly? . . .

5. Why are the Egyptian pharaohs
   famous today? . . .

6. Why are some snakes and some
   spiders dangerous? . . .

a. . . . Because they are made
   of cocoa.

b. . . . Because they built
   the pyramids.

c. . . . Because they are poisonous.

d. . . . Because they sometimes make films
   of the Earth with them.

e. . . . Because there isn't any
   gravity.

f. . . . Because they have very,
   very small wings.

⑧ **Find ten space shuttle words.**

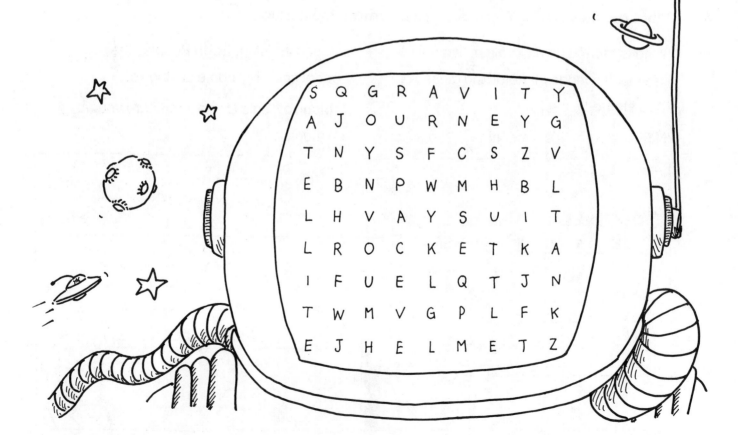

① **Write:** *must* **or** *mustn't.*

CLASS 6A: RULES

1. You _____ stand up and be quiet when the teacher comes into the classroom.
2. You _____ always finish your homework.
3. You _____ play football in the classroom.
4. You _____ bring spiders, snakes or frogs to school.
5. You _____ draw pictures on your desks.
6. You _____ put your English book on the teacher's desk after every lesson.

② **Look at the pictures.   Complete the sentences.**

1.
2.
3.

4.
5.
6.

1. You mustn't _____ here.

2. You mustn't _____ .

3. You must _____ here.

4. You mustn't _____ here.

5. You mustn't _____ here.

6. You must _____ before you eat.

③ **Read the story in your Pupil's Book again.**

Answer: right (√) or wrong (×)?

1. Magixo can't open the box because he can't talk backwards. .... √ ×

2. Magixo wants Uncle John to say a spell and open the box. .... √ ×

3. Uncle John is happy to help Magixo. .... √ ×

4. Magixo goes to find Uncle John's magic wand. .... √ ×

5. Uncle John can't open the box to take the Book of Adabra

    because he doesn't know the spell. .... √ ×

④ **Write the missing words.**

⑤ **Answer the questions.   Use the words in the boxes.**

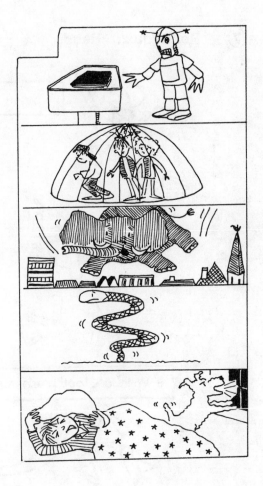

1. Why can't Magixo open the box? | Earth |

   Because he's not an Earth magician.

2. Why can't they escape? | cage |

   _____

3. Why can't elephants fly? | heavy |

   _____

4. Why can't snakes walk? | legs |

   _____

5. Why can't Ken sleep? | bark |

   _____

⑥ **What did they forget?   Write sentences.**

1. Ken *said, ' I forgot my homework.*

   _____

2. Uncle John _____

   _____

3. Caroline _____

   _____

4. Kate _____

   _____

⑦   **Robot quiz.   Read.**

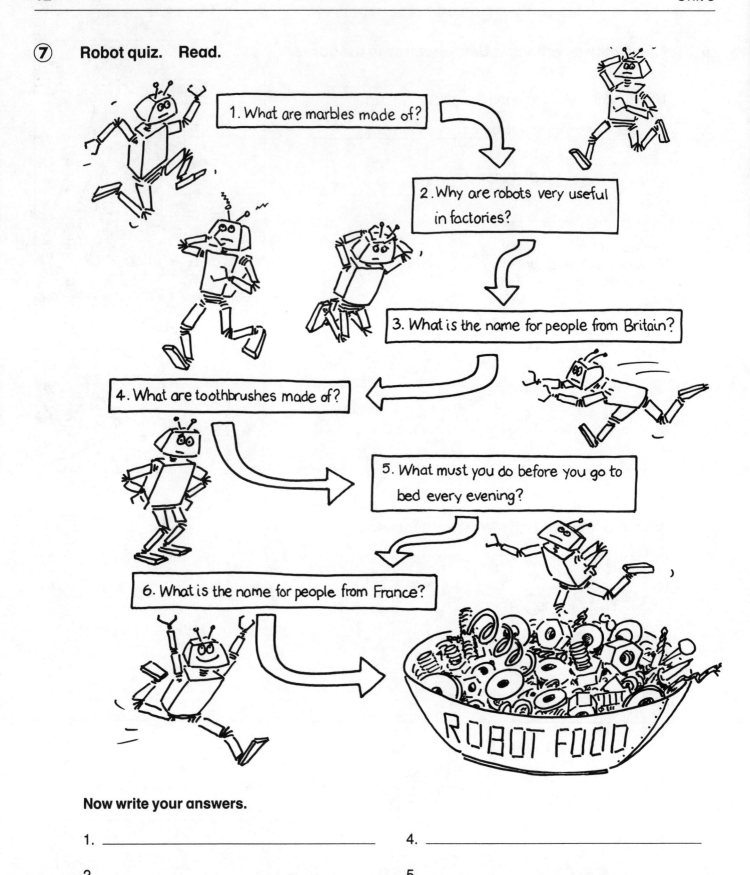

1. What are marbles made of?

2. Why are robots very useful in factories?

3. What is the name for people from Britain?

4. What are toothbrushes made of?

5. What must you do before you go to bed every evening?

6. What is the name for people from France?

ROBOT FOOD

Now write your answers.

1. _____   4. _____

2. _____   5. _____

3. _____   6. _____

① **Answer the questions. Choose A or B.**

1. Which car is cleaner? A or B? _____

2. Which car is older? A or B? _____

3. Which car is bigger? A or B? _____

4. Which skateboard is bigger? A or B? _____

5. Which skateboard is faster? A or B? _____

6. Which skateboard is older? A or B? _____

7. Which snake is fatter? A or B? _____

8. Which snake is longer? A or B? _____

② **Answer the questions.**

Who is sitting next to you? Write his/her name here: [_____]

1. Who is older? You or [_____] ? _____

2. Who is taller? You or [_____] ? _____

3. Who is thinner? You or [_____] ? _____

4. Who is younger? You or [_____] ? _____

5. Who is bigger? You or [_____] ? _____

③   **Read the story in your Pupil's Book again.   Answer the questions.**

1. (Picture 1) Uncle John said, 'We've got the Book of Adabra.
    Now I can read *it*.' What is '*it*'? _____

2. (Picture 2) 'Magixo is coming,' said Ken. 'I can see *him*.'
    Who is '*him*'? _____

3. (Picture 5) 'I didn't like Magixo', said Kate. '*He* was nasty!'
    Who was '*he*'? _____

4. (Picture 6) 'My father was a magician,' Uncle John said, 'and
    he told me about the book.' Who was '*he*'? _____

5. (Picture 8) 'But where are the missing pages?' asked Kate.
    'Who's got *them*?' What is '*them*'? _____

④   **Read and match.**

⑤ **Look at the pictures. Complete the story with words from the box.**

| said | turned | were | sent | put | wanted | came | arrived | were | wanted |

A long time ago, Magixo _____ from Mars to Earth in a big rocket. He _____ in China.

He _____ a special magic spell and he _____ a young Chinese boy into a spider. Then he _____ to turn the spider into a boy again . . . but he didn't know the words!

There _____ some famous magicians in China at that time. Magixo _____ to show them his magic from Mars.

The Chinese magicians _____ very angry. They _____ Magixo back into his rocket and they _____ him back to Mars.

⑥ **Complete the words.**

1. p _ _ _

2. r _ _ _ _ _

ck

5. c _ _ _ _

3. s _ _ _ _

4. c _ _ _ _ _

⑦   **Quiz.   Can you answer these questions?**

1. How many planets are there? _____

2. What is the name for all the planets around the Sun, together? _____

3. What is the name of the third planet from the Sun? _____

4. How many kilometres is the Earth from the Sun? _____

5. How many planets in the Solar System are smaller than the Earth,
    and what are their names? _____

6. How many planets in the Solar System are bigger than the Earth,
    and what are their names? _____

⑧   **Find the names of the Sun and its nine planets.**

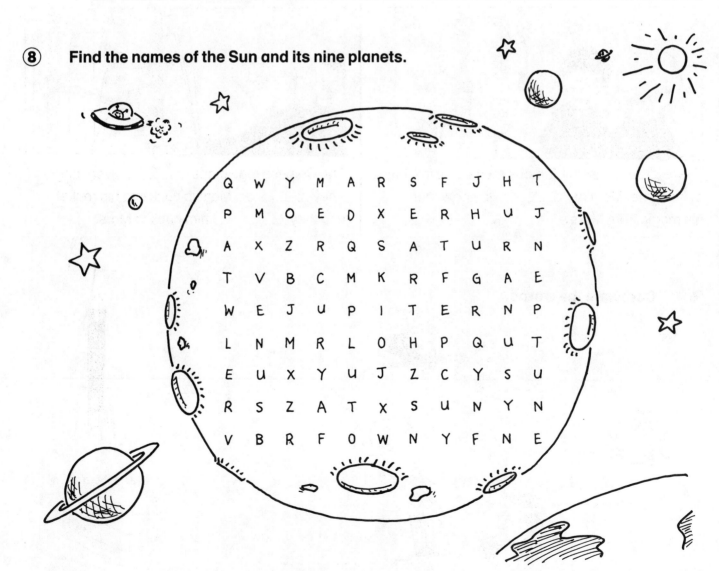

```
Q  W  Y  M  A  R  S  F  J  H  T
P  M  O  E  D  X  E  R  H  U  J
A  X  Z  R  Q  S  A  T  U  R  N
T  V  B  C  M  K  R  F  G  A  E
W  E  J  U  P  I  T  E  R  N  P
L  N  M  R  L  O  H  P  Q  U  T
E  U  X  Y  U  J  Z  C  Y  S  U
R  S  Z  A  T  X  S  U  N  Y  N
V  B  R  F  O  W  N  Y  F  N  E
```

① **The children are having a party.   They are putting on funny clothes.**
What are they going to be?   Match the pictures.

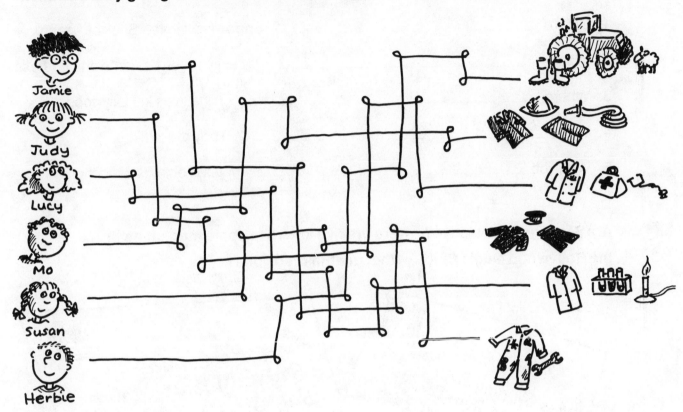

Now write sentences.

1. Jamie *is going to be a bus driver* .

2. Judy _____ .

3. Lucy _____ .

4. Mo _____ .

5. Susan _____ .

6. Herbie _____ .

② **Read.   Then answer the questions.**

1. Frank works in a shop. He sells books, postcards
   and newspapers. What's his job? _____

2. Janet works in an office in a big hospital. She types letters
   and talks to people on the telephone. What's her job? _____

3. Angela does interesting experiments with rabbits in
   a laboratory. What's her job? _____

4. Mike drives a fire-engine and he puts out fires in buildings.
   What's his job? _____

③ **Read the story in your Pupil's Book again.**

Look at the answers. Then complete the questions.

1. Where _____ ? She found it in the Book of Adabra.

2. Whose _____ ? Lucky Lorenz's name and address.

3. Where _____ ? She lives in Hollywood.

4. What _____ ? They make films.

5. What job _____ ? Miss Electra is a teacher.

④ **Are you a good detective?   Here are five letters to some magicians in the Hollywood Magic Club.   What are their real jobs?**

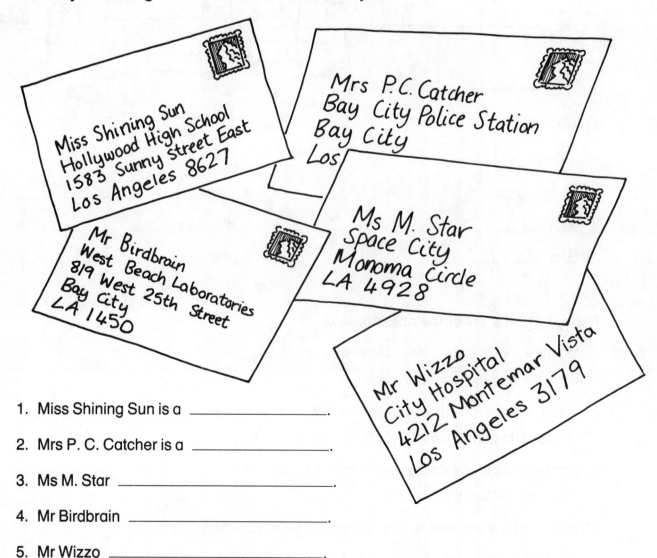

1. Miss Shining Sun is a _____ .

2. Mrs P. C. Catcher is a _____ .

3. Ms M. Star _____ .

4. Mr Birdbrain _____ .

5. Mr Wizzo _____ .

⑤   Look at the picture.   Who lives here?   Write sentences.

| artist   builder   cook   dancer   farmer   postman   secretary |

1. *The postman lives* _____ at number 1.   5. _____

2. _____ at number 2.   6. _____

3. _____   7. _____

4. _____   8. _____

⑥   Now answer these questions.

1. Who lives opposite the cook? _____

2. Who lives between the builder and the postman? _____

3. Who lives next to the artist? _____

4. Who lives opposite the artist? _____

5. Who lives next to the doctor? _____

⑦   **Answer the questions.**

1. What does your father do? _____

2. What does your mother do? _____

3. What does your uncle do? _____

4. What does your aunt do? _____

5. What do your brothers or sisters do? _____

⑧   **Complete the crossword.**

① **Write three words together.**

sadder	heavier	better	biggest	saddest	~~tall~~
longest	shortest	heaviest	big	long	
~~tallest~~	thinner	best	good	fatter	~~taller~~
thin	fat	short	heavy	shorter	sad
bigger	fattest	longer	thinnest		

1. _tall, taller, tallest_

2. _____

3. _____

4. _____

5. _____

6. _____

7. _____

8. _____

9. _____

② **Look at the animals. Answer: right (√) or wrong (×)?**

1. A is thinner than C. .... √ ×

2. B is fatter than C. .... √ ×

3. C is the fattest of the three. ..... √ ×

4. M is the tallest giraffe. .... √ ×

5. L is shorter than M. .... √ ×

6. K is taller than L. .... √ ×

7. X is the happiest of the three. ... √ ×

8. Y is happier than Z. .... √ ×

9. Z is happier than X. .... √ ×

③   **Read the story in your Pupil's Book again.**
    Make sentences with these words.

1. Mr Wizzo / best / magician _____

2. Ken / biggest / piece / Mr Wizzo's cake _____

3. Mr Wizzo / oldest magician / the world _____

4. The Book of Adabra / older / Mr Wizzo _____

5. Lucky Lorenz / famous / woman magician / Hollywood _____

_____

④   **Look at the pictures.   Answer the questions.**

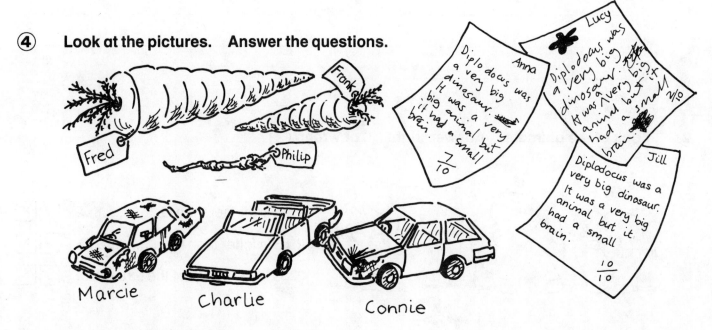

1. Is Philip a better farmer than Frank? _____

2. Who is the best farmer? _____

3. Which is the best carrot? _____

4. Which is the best of the three letters? _____

5. Is Lucy a better pupil than Jill? _____

6. Is Anna a better pupil than Lucy? _____

7. Is Connie a better driver than Charlie? _____

8. Who has got the best car? _____

⑤   **Where are the children?   Complete the sentences.**

Use the words: *between, opposite, next to*.

1. Suzy is in studio 10, *next to the cinema.*

2. Sammy is in studio _____

3. Sally _____

4. Billy _____

5. Betty _____

6. Bobby _____

6   **Write the answers in the boxes.   Then answer the questions.**

You	Your friend

How tall are you? (in centimetres)

How heavy are you? (in kilograms)

How fast can you run 100 metres? (in seconds)

How fast can you say the ABC in English? (in seconds)

How long is your hair? (in centimetres)

How many letters are there in your name?

1. Who is taller? You or your friend? _____

2. Who is heavier? You or your friend? _____

3. Who can run faster? You or your friend? _____

4. Who can say the ABC in English faster? You or your friend? _____

5. Who has got shorter hair? You or your friend? _____

6. Who has got a longer name? You or your friend? _____

7   **Answer the questions.**

1. Who is the tallest boy or girl in your class? _____

2. Who is the fastest runner in your class? _____

3. Who has got the longest hair in your class? _____

4. Who is the cleverest boy or girl in your class? _____

5. Who is the most beautiful filmstar in the world? _____

6. Who is the best pop star in the world? _____

① **Look at the pictures.   What did Kate and Ken do yesterday?**

What are they going to do tomorrow?

Now write Kate's diary.   Today is Friday.

Thursday

We went _____

_____ in the morning.

_____

_____ in the afternoon.

_____

_____ in the evening.

Friday

Saturday

We're going to _____

_____ in the morning.

_____

_____ in the afternoon.

_____

_____ in the evening.

② **Answer the questions.**

1. What did you do yesterday?

   morning: _____

   _____

   afternoon: _____

   _____

   evening: _____

   _____

2. What are you going to do tomorrow?

   morning: _____

   _____

   afternoon: _____

   _____

   evening: _____

   _____

③ **Read the story in your Pupil's Book again.**

Then tell the story again.   Use these sentences.

> They saw some filmstars.
> They were making a cowboy film.

> The cowboys' guns were not real.

> The tall cowboy killed the short cowboy with his gun

> Uncle John took the children to a film studio in Hollywood.

> They found Lucky Lorenz in a room near studio 3.

> There was a tall cowboy and a short cowboy in the film.

> The short cowboy stood up again and laughed.

Uncle John took the children _____

_____

_____

_____

_____

_____

④ **Read and match the pictures with the words from the cowboy films.**

> Hands up! keep them up and don't move.

> No! No! Please! Please don't kill me. What... What do you want?

Picture _____

2
> Ok, friend. Where's the money? Tell me. Quick!

> It ... It's in that box over there... under my bed, near the door.

Picture _____

3
> Mmm...Beans. That's my favourite food. Beans...

> Shh! Listen. Do you hear? A horse. Someone's coming. We must hide!

Picture _____

⑤ **What's going to happen?   Write sentences.**

The postman is going to give Ken a present.   _____

_____

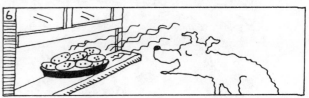

_____

⑥ **Kate, Judy and Jamie are talking about their marbles.   Read.**

Complete the boxes.   Then answer the questions.

	Number of marbles			
	blue	white	green	total
Kate				
Judy				
Jamie				

1. Who's got more marbles than Kate? _____

2. Who's got the most blue marbles? _____

3. Who's got the most green marbles? _____

4. Who's got the most white marbles? _____

⑦ **Complete the crossword.   Find the name of the bank robber.**

1. The robber went into the . . . . . , in the centre of Chicago.

2. He had a big . . . . . moustache.

3. His moustache was not a . . . . . one.

4. The . . . . . think the robber came from Denver.

5. He . . . . . a man and a woman in the bank.

6. After he left the bank, he put a big black . . . . . on his head.

7. He took thousands of . . . . . and some jewellery from the bank.

8. He dropped an old . . . . . from Denver to Chicago on the floor of the bank.

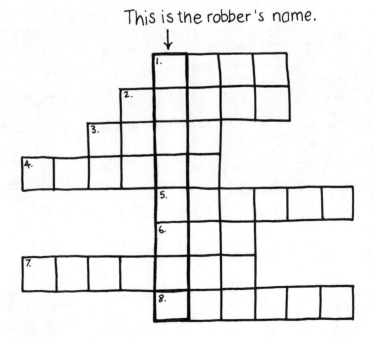

This is the robber's name.

① **Read the menu.**

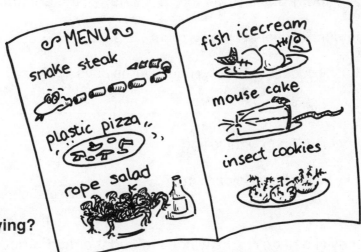

What are they saying?

Write the words.

1.

Would you *like some plastic pizza*   ?

Yes, please.

2.

_____ ?

No, _____ . I'd like

3.

_____ ?

4.

_____ ?

② **Read the story in your Pupil's Book again.   Answer the questions.**

1. What did Ken want to wear in Lucky's room? _____

2. Who asked Lucky about the missing pages three days ago? _____

3. Where is Spider Smith now? _____

4. What do Spider and Ringo want to find? _____

5. What did Lucky think about Spider Smith? _____

③ **Where would they like to go?   Draw lines to find the right places.**

Write what they say.

1. Caroline says, *'I'd like to go to* _____ ,'

2. Kate says, '_____ ,'

3. Ken says, '_____ ,'

4. Uncle John says, '_____ ,'

5. Spider Smith says, '_____ ,'

④   What are they saying?   Complete the sentences.

Kate: Would you like _to wear these trousers_ ?

Ken: No, thank you, _they're too long._ .

Kate: Would you like _____ ?

Caroline: No, _____ .

Kate: Would you like _____ ?

Uncle John: No, _____ .

Uncle John: _____ to wear these?

They're magic!

Children: Yes, please!

⑤   Complete the words.

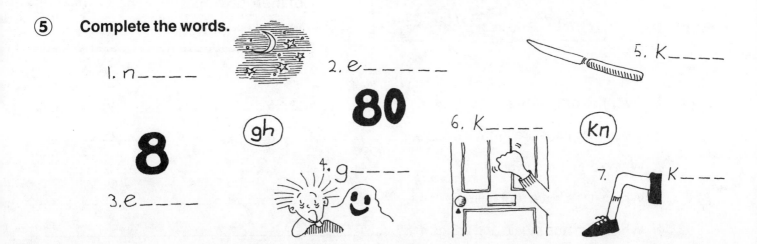

1. n _ _ _ _

2. e _ _ _ _ _

3. e _ _ _ _

4. g _ _ _ _

5. k _ _ _ _

6. k _ _ _ _

7. k _ _ _

⑥   **Read and match.   Write the letters in the boxes.**

1

This 50-minute MGM film has
all your favourite cartoon animals
in it: Roger Rabbit, Donald Duck
and Mickey Mouse.
Wonderful fun for young people
and old people too!   ☐

2

This is one of Disney's most
famous films: it tells the story
of a wild animal's adventures
in the big bad city.   ☐

3

One of the funniest films in the
world: real birds talking, singing,
dancing and doing tricks.
You <u>must</u> see it!   ☐

4

The James Brothers always ride
together. Their black horses and
their silver guns are famous . . .
and frightening. This is the story
of their adventures in the Wild
West of America.   ☐

⑦   **Answer the questions.**

1. Which two films are funny? _____

2. Which one is a cowboy film? _____

3. Which films have real animals in them? _____

4. Which film has music and songs in it? _____

① **Look into your crystal ball.**

Then answer the children's questions about next week.

NEXT WEEK FOR YOU

... buy some purple socks.

...see a ghost outside the window one night.

...win an important game or quiz.

... go to sleep in a maths lesson at school.

...fall off your bicycle or skateboard.

...find a big spider in your bed or in your shoes.

...meet a dinosaur in the street near your house.

...forget to go to a friend's birthday party.

... have an adventure in the park.

...hear some interesting news on TV.

...go on a long journey - to Mars, perhaps.

...see a famous filmstar.

1.  What will I do next week?

You'll _____

2. What will I do next week?

3. What will I do next week?

4. What will I do next week?

5.  What will I do next week?

6. What will I do next week?

7.  What will I do next week?

8.  What will I do next week?

◆ And you? What will <u>you</u> do next week? _____

② **Read the story in your Pupil's Book again.**

Look at the answers.   Then complete the questions.

1. _____? They were in the middle of Australia.

2. _____? He was with Ringo Dingo.

3. _____? Ringo stole it from Kashoki.

4. _____? There was a shopping list inside the box.

5. _____? Spider must talk to Kashoki.

③ **Class Six is going to have a beach party.   What are the children saying?**

Match the pictures.   Then write their words.

1. Mo says, '*I'll bring some icecreams* _____.'

2. Judy says, '_____.'

3. Jamie says, '_____.'

4. Susan says, '_____.'

5. Herbie says, '_____.'

6. Lucy says, '_____.'

④   **Complete the sentences.   Use words from the box.**

> Verbs: painting laughing whispering shouting
> Adverbs: angrily quietly carelessly happily

1.

Mr Jones is _____ .

2.

Mrs Jones is _____ .

3.

Jane is _____ .

4.

John is _____ .

⑤   **Complete the diary.   Use words from the box.**

> quickly found island frightened teeth saw looked than climbed chased found left

17th June

Today I went on the _____ . I _____ crocodiles with sharp _____ , chimpanzees, snakes and more _____ one hundred parrots! One crocodile _____ me, but I ran _____ and _____ a tree. I was very _____ .

The crocodile _____ . Then I _____ a treasure map inside a hole in the tree. With the map, I _____ a cave. I _____ inside it.

It was full of treasure!

⑥   **Complete the crossword.**

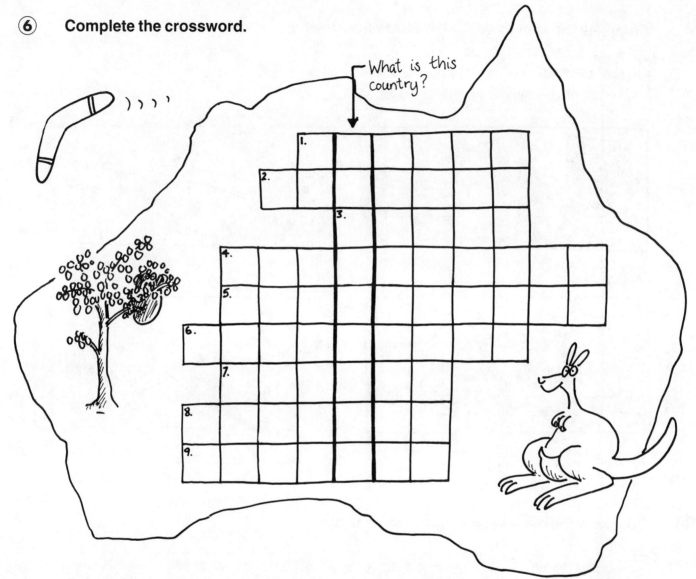

1. Kangaroos carry their . . . . . in a special pocket, called a 'pouch'.

2. The centre of the . . . . . is a desert.

3. Australian farmers have many . . . . . on their farms.

4. Australia is one of the seven . . . . . of the world.

5. The . . . . . were the first people in Australia.

6. . . . . . have strong legs and tails – they can jump very high.

7. . . . . . are smaller than kangaroos – they climb trees.

8. The people in Australia speak . . . .

9. The desert in the centre of the country is called the '. . . . .'.

Look at these shapes.   What do they look like?
Write sentences.

1.

This looks like a flower.

2.

3.

4.

5.

6.

② What do these people look like?   Write sentences.

1.

She looks like

2.

3.

4.

5.

③   **Read the story in your Pupil's Book again.   Answer the questions.**

1. 'We must talk to Kashoki before Spider gets *there*,' said
   Uncle John. Where is '*there*'? _____

2. 'You want the missing pages . . . ,' said Ringo, 'but you're
   not going to get *them*!' What was '*them*'? _____

3. *They* saw the crocodiles under *them*.
   Who were '*they*' and '*them*'? _____

4. The bridge opened and they fell through *it*. What was '*it*'? _____

5. 'Put *him* in the kangaroo cage,' said Ken. Who was '*him*'? _____

④   **Alphabet quiz.   Choose the right word.**

1. Which E is the biggest?   a. egg   b. envelope   c. elephant
2. Which L is the heaviest?   a. lorry   b. lion   c. lemon
3. Which C is the fastest?   a. calendar   b. crisps   c. car
4. Which S is the most dangerous? a. sheep   b. song   c. snake
5. Which M is the shortest?   a. match   b. mile   c. man
6. Which P is the oldest?   a. photo   b. pyramid   c. phone
7. Which H is the tallest?   a. horse   b. housewife   c. helmet

⑤   **Complete the words.**

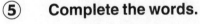

b _ _ _ _ _ _ _   f _ _ _ _   d _ _ _ _ _ _ _   a _ _ _ _ _ _ _

(ui)   (au)   t _ _ _ _ _   _ _ _ _

m _ _ _ _   m _ _ _ _   (ur)   n _ _ _ _

(ic)

⑥ **Look at the pictures.   Write the story.   Use words from the boxes.**

1.

in jungle / in Africa / near river / under tree

2.

. . . looks like a crocodile / must leave quickly

3.

turned its head / opened its mouth

4.

rock / water-bottle / started to have a drink

5.

Suddenly / started to move / looked at it / small eyes! . . . big mouth!

6.

up in tall tree / went for a swim in the river

Ringo Dingo and Spider Smith were in the jungle, in Africa.

⑦ **Read.**

There are more than 250 different types of shark in the sea. The smallest sharks are called 'dog fish'. They are about one metre long. The largest shark is the enormous 'whale shark'. It is about eighteen metres from nose to tail.

A whale shark
18 metres (1800 centimetres)

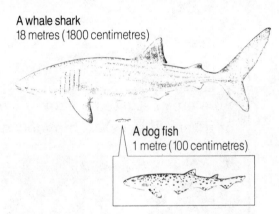

A dog fish
1 metre (100 centimetres)

Sharks have very good noses – they find their food with their noses. They <u>smell</u> their food under the water, and then they swim to catch it.

Sharks have very strong tails. Some sharks can swim very fast with their strong tails, but other sharks are slower. The big whale shark cannot swim very fast.

Sharks have very strong, sharp teeth too. They usually catch and eat other, smaller fish, but sometimes they attack people swimming in warmer water near the beach. Sharks are the most dangerous animals in the sea!

The great white shark has strong, sharp teeth

Now answer the questions.

1. How long are the largest sharks? _____

2. How do sharks find their food? _____

3. Why can some sharks swim very fast? _____

4. What do sharks usually eat? _____

5. Why are sharks the most dangerous animals in the sea? _____

① **Look at these toys. Then complete the sentences.**

1. How much are the monster masks?   They're _____.

2. How much is the toy aeroplane?   It's _____.

3. _____ ?   It's £8.40.

4. _____ ?   It's £5.90.

5. _____ ?   They're £15.50.

6. _____ ?   It's £12.25.

② **Read the story in your Pupil's Book again.   Make sentences with these words.**

1. went / Japan / Time Machine _____

2. walked / Kashoki's house / Japanese park _____

3. Spider Smith / tree / in the park _____

4. Uncle John / Kashoki / Book of Adabra _____

5. Kashoki / told / go backwards / 2500 BC _____

③ **Look at Mr Kashoki's address.**

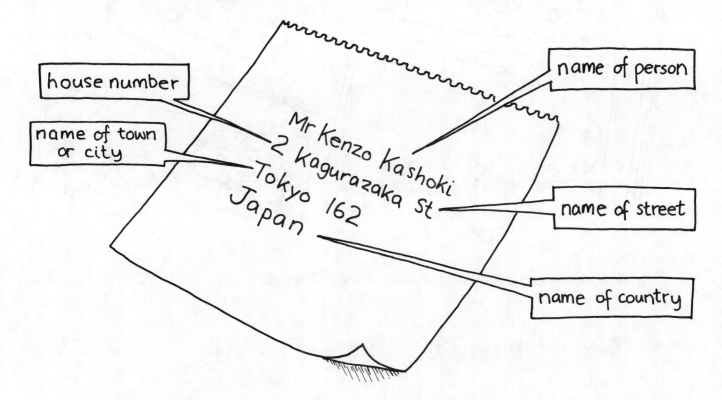

Now write your address here.   **And write your friend's address here.**

④ **Puzzle.   Where do the presents come from?**
Write sentences about the pictures.

1. ZARLIB

2. HINCA

3. IANTRIB

4. EGRECE

5. ASIRUS

6. ANSIP

1. *The mask comes from Brazil. It's Brazilian.*

2. _____

3. _____

4. _____

5. _____

_____

⑤ **Write these sentences again to match the pictures.**

The mouse ran up the clock.

Four mice ran up two clocks.

The woman bought a knife.

_____

The man read a story.

_____

The sheep chased the child.

_____

⑥ Answer these questions about <u>your</u> country.

1. Where is your country? Which continent is it in?

   _____

2. What other countries are near your country?

   _____

3. What is the capital of your country?

   _____

4. What other large towns or cities are there?

   _____

5. What kinds of special food do you eat in your country?

   _____

6. What sports do people play in your country?

   _____

7. What important things do people make and sell in your country?

   _____

⑦ Find twelve words about Japan.

These words are on page 44 in your Pupil's Book.

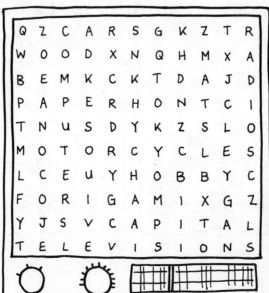

Q	Z	C	A	R	S	G	K	Z	T	R
W	O	O	D	X	N	Q	H	M	X	A
B	E	M	K	C	K	T	D	A	J	D
P	A	P	E	R	H	O	N	T	C	I
T	N	U	S	D	Y	K	Z	S	L	O
M	O	T	O	R	C	Y	C	L	E	S
L	C	E	U	Y	H	O	B	B	Y	C
F	O	R	I	G	A	M	I	X	G	Z
Y	J	S	V	C	A	P	I	T	A	L
T	E	L	E	V	I	S	I	O	N	S

① **Read and match.**

1. I'm late for school, so . . .

2. I'm hungry, so . . .

3. I can't find my pen, so . . .

4. I've got his address, so . . .

5. It was Mum's birthday, so . . .

6. There was a hole in my pocket, so . . .

7. There were sharks in the sea, so . . .

8. They wanted to find the pyramid, so . . .

a. . . . I can write to him now.

b. . . . I can't do my homework.

c. . . . we didn't go swimming.

d. . . . I lost all my money.

e. . . . I must run quickly.

f. . . . I gave them Kashoki's map.

g. . . . I bought her a present.

h. . . . I'm going to eat some bread and honey now.

② **Magic sentence tricks.** **Write the sentences again with *so*.**

I'll take an umbrella with me because it's raining.

It's raining so I'll take an umbrella with me.

1. You can't bend it because it's made of metal.

_____

2. She speaks French and English because she comes from Canada.

_____

3. Astronauts float around in space because there isn't any gravity.

_____

4. Crocodiles are dangerous because they have sharp teeth.

_____

5. Film directors today make more exciting films because they can use

many special effects. _____

③   **Read the story in your Pupil's Book again.**

Now tell the story again.   Use these sentences.

> The magician climbed into the basket . . . and he disappeared. The Queen was afraid.

> When they arrived in Egypt, they saw the River Nile and an enormous new pyramid, made of stone.

> The magician had the Book of Adabra in his hand. He did a dangerous trick from the Book with some poisonous snakes in a basket.

> Spider Smith hid behind the seats inside the Time Machine, and so he went from Australia to Egypt with Uncle John and the children.

> Queen Neops and her magician were at the new pyramid. The magician wanted to show the Queen some new magic tricks.

Spider Smith hid behind

_____

_____

_____

_____

④   **Look at this puzzle message from Queen Neops.**

Match the numbers and the words.   Write the sentences.

1 come	2 cat	3 Venus	4 party	5 sky	6 Bring
7 We'll	8 Please	9 o'clock	10 and	11 your	12 to
13 Dead	14 the	15 is	16 famous	17 all	18 my
19 eat	20 one	21 at	22 black	23 Pyramid	24 cookies
25 ghost	26 have	27 when	28 Pharaoh	29 in	
30 of	31 friends	32 food			

8 / 1 / 12 / 18 / 25 / 4.   6 / 17 / 11 / 31.

_____

7 / 26 / 22 / 2 / 24 / 10 / 16 / 28 / 32 / 12 / 19.

_____

1 / 12 / 14 / 23 / 30 / 14 / 13 / 21 / 20 / 9, / 27 / 3 / 15 / 29 / 14 / 5.

_____

⑤   The pyramids.   Complete the sentences.   Use words from the box.

museum	rocks	pyramids	food	stole	front	so
treasure	city	built	gold	inside	thousand	put

Five _____ years ago, the Ancient Egyptians _____ very large buildings called _____ for the king or pharaoh. The Egyptians _____ the dead pharaoh inside the pyramid. They put _____ for the pharaoh too, and beautiful chairs and tables and statues and jewellery made of _____ . But sometimes robbers found these things _____ the pyramid and they _____ the dead pharaoh's treasures.

So some pharaohs did not want pyramids. The Egyptians put these pharaohs under a big hill. Then they put rocks in _____ of the doors, _____ nobody opened them for thousands of years.

One day, in 1922, an English man had a surprise. He found a door under some _____ . He went inside and found the _____ of Tutankhamun, a young pharaoh. The treasure was beautiful.

Today you can see the treasure of Tutankhamun in the _____ of Cairo, the capital _____ of Egypt.

⑥   Look at Tutankhamun's treasure.   Complete the words.

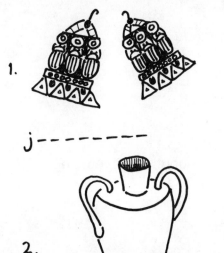

1.

j _ _ _ _ _ _ _

2.

v _ _ _

3.

m _ _ _

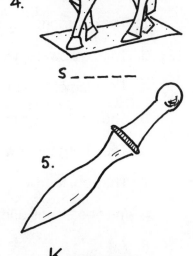

4.

s _ _ _ _ _

5.

k _ _ _ _

⑦ **Read the sentences and complete the pyramid.**

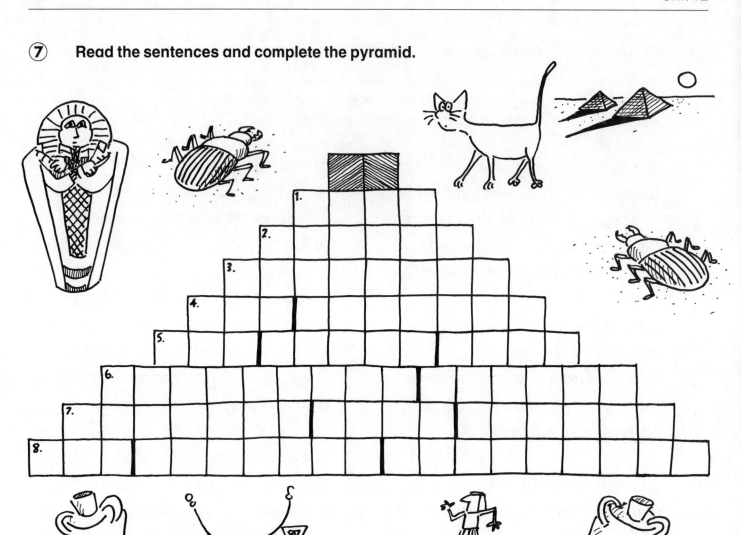

1. The kings and queens of Ancient Egypt had jewellery made of . . . .

2. The pharaohs had beautiful clothes made of wool or . . . .

3. The . . . . . were houses for the dead Egyptian pharaohs.

4. The king of the Ancient Egyptians was called . . . .

5. The Ancient Egyptians lived near . . . . , about 5,000 years ago.

6. The pharaohs' jewellery was made of gold and . . . .

7. They put food, ... , ... , ... and chairs for

   the dead kings and queens inside the pyramids.

8. . . . . lived near the Nile, because they needed its water for

   their farms.

① **Match the people and the countries and the plane, train or boat.**

Then write sentences.

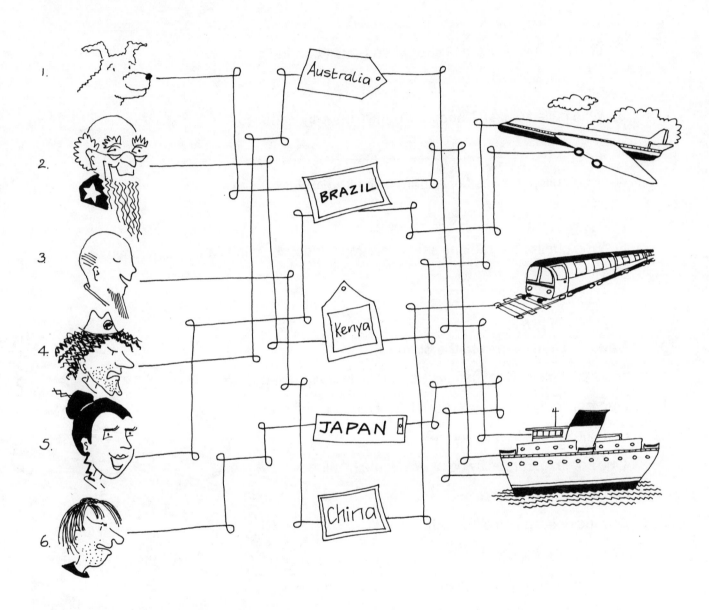

1. Barker *went to Brazil by boat.*

2. Mr Wizzo

3.

4.

5.

6.

② **Read the story in your Pupil's Book again.   Answer the questions.**

1. Where was the Queen's magician when they saw him again?

   _____

2. What came out of the basket when Spider opened it?

   _____

3. Who pulled Queen Neops away from the angry snakes?

   _____

4. Who pulled the Book of Adabra away from Spider Smith?

   _____

5. Who put the box with the seven missing pages inside the Queen's pyramid?

   _____

③ **Read.   Then complete the boxes.**

Joanna, Jane and John are in Europe on holiday. They all come from

different countries – one comes from Canada, one comes from America

and one comes from China.

 One came to Europe by boat, one came by plane

and one came by train.

 Joanna doesn't come from America.

 The boy comes from China.

 The Canadian came by plane.

 The one from America came by boat.

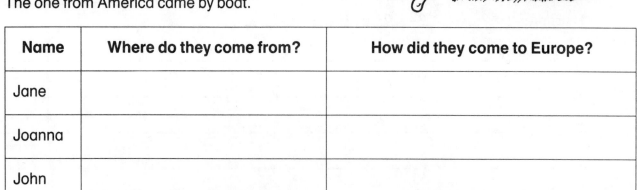

Name	Where do they come from?	How did they come to Europe?
Jane		
Joanna		
John		

④　**Complete the sentences.　Put the verbs into the past tense.**

Rich Ancient Egyptian people ____ (have) lots of parties. Before the party, men and women ____ (put on) their best clothes and their favourite jewellery.

People often ____ (take) their pet animals to the party – cats, dogs and sometimes monkeys. Everybody ____ (listen) to music and ____ (watch) dancers. When the dancers ____ (do) clever tricks, people ____ (laugh) and ____ (clap).

What food did the Ancient Egyptians like to eat at parties? They ____ (like) meat, cheese, fruit and bread. They ____ (eat) a lot of fish too.

⑤　**Magic Numbers.　Look at this code.　Find Caroline's number.**

A	B	C	D	E	F	G	H	I	J	K	L	M	N	O	P	Q	R	S	T	U	V	W	X	Y	Z
1	2	3	4	5	6	7	8	9	10	11	12	13	14	15	16	17	18	19	20	21	22	23	24	25	26

J	K	L	M	N	O	P	Q	R	S
1+0	1+1	1+2	1+3	1+4	1+5	1+6	1+7	1+8	1+9
1	2	3	4	5	6	7	8	9	10

S	T	U	V	W	X	Y	Z
1+0	2+0						
1	2	3	4	5	6	7	8

My magic number is
k e n
2 + 5 + 5 = 12 = 1 + 2 = 3 !

My magic number is
k a t e
2 + 1 + 2 + 5 = 10 = 1 + 0 = 1

Can you help me?
My magic number is
C a r o l i n e
_ _ _ _ _ _ _ _ =

◆ What's your magic number?

⑥ **Here is a page from a letter from Spider Smith to Ringo Dingo.**
Can you read it?

I visited you in Australia, I went to Egypt [blotted] John Jones in his magic Time Machine.

[blotted] we arrived in Egypt, we saw the Queen with her magician. The magician had the Book of Adabra. He did a very clever trick — he [blotted] disappeared [blotted] a basket of snakes.

[blotted] I looked into the basket. The Book was in there, so I [blotted] took it [blotted] I ran to the river. But Barker, that nasty little dog, attacked me [blotted] I fell [blotted] the river.

Write Spider's letter again here.   Use words from the box.

suddenly and Then After quickly into and When inside with

_____

_____

_____

_____

_____

_____

_____

_____

_____

_____

① **Read and find the treasures on the island.**

Always start in the middle of the map.

NORTH

some pretty flowers

some gold coins

a book of magic spells

an Ancient Chinese vase

a colourful mask

a black cat

a magic hat

a tall tree

some old English stamps

a river with crocodiles

some poisonous spiders

an old Spanish painting

a dangerous jungle

a family of chimpanzees

WEST

some purple rocks

START HERE

some guns

EAST

a tree-house

Some Ancient Greek jewellery

a silver spear

wild horses

a basket of food

some enormous snakes

a dead tree

a wild elephant

a crystal bottle

some poisonous powder

a magic bird

an Ancient Japanese mask

SOUTH

1. Walk three squares to the east. Turn north and go five squares. Then turn west and go two squares. What do you find there? __Some gold coins__

2. Walk three squares to the west. Turn south and go two squares. What do you find there? _____

3. Walk four squares south. Turn east and walk three squares, then go one square south. What do you find there? _____

4. Go two squares north. Turn east and go two squares. What do you find there? _____

5. Walk two squares north. Turn west and go four squares, across a river with crocodiles in it. Then turn north and walk two squares. What do you find there? _____

6. Go one square north. Turn east and go five squares through some dangerous jungle. Stop and say 'Hello' to the family of chimpanzees. Then turn north and go four squares. What do you find? _____

② **Read the story in your Pupil's Book again.   Make sentences with these words.**

1. Uncle John and the children / inside / pyramid _____

2. saw / boxes of gold coins / big room _____

3. Suddenly / fell into / big hole / hundreds / snakes in it _____

4. Spider Smith / looked down / in the hole / laughed _____

5. children and Uncle John / waited / listened _____

③ **What are they afraid of?**

Look at the chart.   Then write sentences.

	lots of homework	spiders	the dark	ghosts	angry teachers	insects	snakes	big dogs	water
Ken	✓		✓		✓	✓			
Caroline		✓		✓			✓		
Kate		✓		✓		✓			
Uncle John								✓	

1. Ken *is afraid of lots of homework, the dark, angry teachers and insects. He isn't afraid of ghosts.*

2. Caroline _____

3. Kate _____

4. Uncle John _____

◆ **What are you afraid of?   Write sentences.**

_____

_____

④   **Write a story.**   *Spider Smith followed Uncle John and the children when they went into the pyramid. He came to a big strong door made of wood. He opened the door quietly and.....*

Look at the pictures. Complete the story with words from the boxes.

table / chairs / middle of a / small room / gold plates / cups / food

ran and ran / dark / no candle / Suddenly / big room / black hole in the middle

went in / Suddenly / ghost / stood up / pointed angrily / Spider turned / ran

went / looked down into / started to laugh

_____

_____

_____

_____

⑤   **Complete the words.**

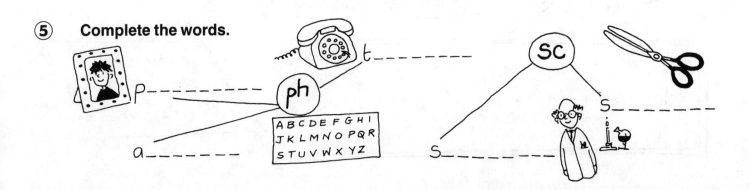

p _ _ _ _ _ _

t _ _ _ _ _ _

a _ _ _ _ _ _

s _ _ _ _ _

s _ _ _ _ _ _

ABCDEFGHI
JKLMNOPQR
STUVWXYZ

⑥   Which word is different?   Choose the word.

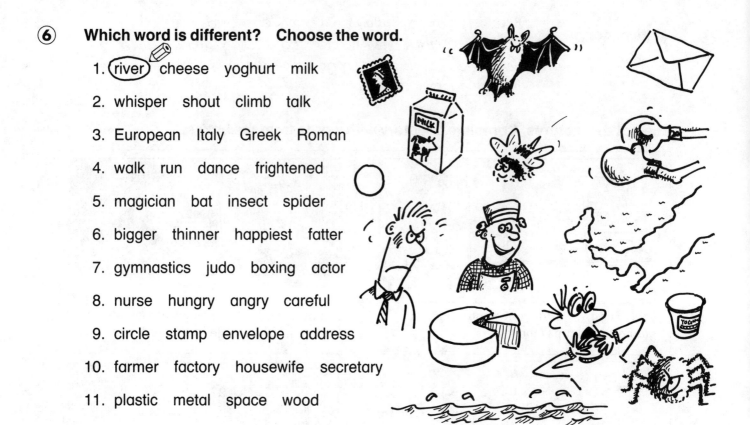

1. (river) cheese yoghurt milk
2. whisper shout climb talk
3. European Italy Greek Roman
4. walk run dance frightened
5. magician bat insect spider
6. bigger thinner happiest fatter
7. gymnastics judo boxing actor
8. nurse hungry angry careful
9. circle stamp envelope address
10. farmer factory housewife secretary
11. plastic metal space wood

**⑦   Write the time words inside the clock.   Write the job words on the computer.
Write the new animal words in the cage.**

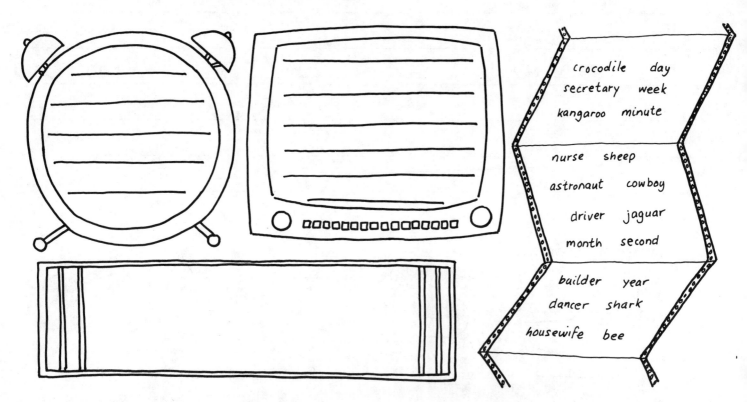

crocodile   day
secretary   week
kangaroo   minute

nurse   sheep
astronaut   cowboy
driver   jaguar
month   second

builder   year
dancer   shark
housewife   bee

① **Complete the sentences with the right adjective.**

1. This one is the ___*heaviest*___ (heavy) of the three bags.

2. Caroline's hair is _____ (short) than Kate's.

3. Judy is the _____ (pretty) girl in our class.

4. His painting is _____ (good) than Zoko's.

5. I think that story is _____ (interesting) than this one.

6. Which one is the _____ (famous) of the four filmstars?

7. This is the _____ (good) restaurant in the city.

② **What do you think they'll do?**

Write: *Yes, they will.* **or** *No, they won't.*

1. Will the snakes attack Uncle John and the children? _____

2. Will Spider Smith run away with the Book of Adabra? _____

3. Will the children climb out of the hole? _____

4. Will Spider Smith help Uncle John and the children? _____

5. Will Uncle John say a magic spell and turn one of the

   snakes into a ladder? _____

③ **Find ten irregular verbs in the past tense in the square.**

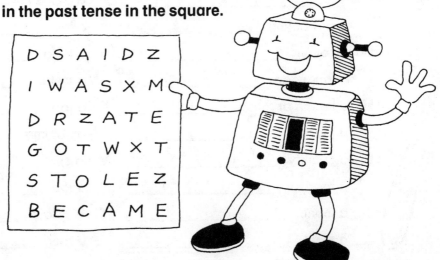

```
D S A I D Z
I W A S X M
D R Z A T E
G O T W X T
S T O L E Z
B E C A M E
```

④ **Read the story in your Pupil's Book again.   Answer the questions.**

1. Who helped Uncle John and the children to climb out of the hole? _____

2. What did Caroline take out of Queen Neops's box? _____

3. What did they all do when they were back in the Time Machine? _____

4. Where did they get out of the Time Machine when they arrived

   back in London? _____

5. Who gave Kate's mum some flowers at the end? _____

⑤ **A B C words quiz. Write the words next to the letters.**

A a fruit _apple_____   **L** a room _____
  a continent _____   a job _____

B a sport _____   **M** a planet _____
  a country _____   a drink _____

C a place in town _____   **N** a job _____
  an animal _____   a number _____

D a month _____   **O** a place (in a building) _____
  a job _____   a fruit _____

E a number _____   **P** a bird _____
  a planet _____   a colour _____

F a job _____   **R** a place in town _____
  a sea animal _____   a toy _____

G a colour _____   **S** a food _____
  a language _____   a metal _____

H a lesson at school _____   **T** a job _____
  a place in town _____   an animal _____

I a country _____   **V** a sport _____
  a food _____   a job _____

J a month _____   **Y** a colour _____
  a sport _____   a food _____

⑥   **Complete the crossword.**

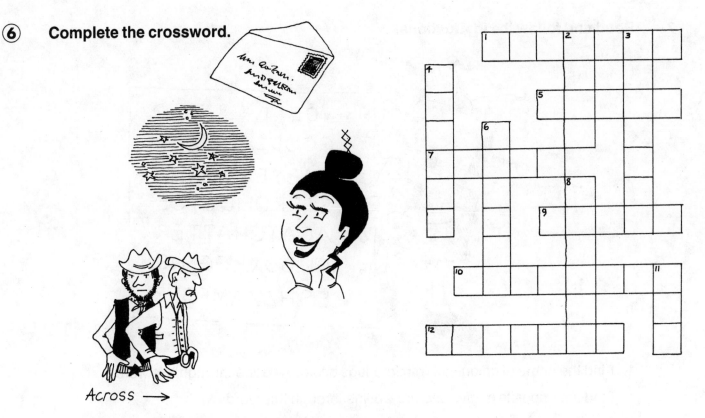

Across →

1. 'Mars', 'Venus' and 'Pluto' are the names of three . . . . . .

5. Uncle John and the children went to see Kashoki in . . . . . .

7. The pyramids in Egypt are made of . . . . . .

9. When you look at the sky at night, you can usually see thousands of . . . . . .

10. The . . . . . were houses for the dead kings and queens of Ancient Egypt.

12. We call people from Spain ' . . . . . ' people.

Down ↓

2. The pyramid was . . . . . the River Nile.

3. Miss Electra, the magician, is usually a . . . . . .

4. Cowboys usually ride . . . . . .

6. One . . . . . wanted to kill the other one with his gun.

8. Before you send a letter, you must put some . . . . . on the envelope.

11. The nine planets in the Solar System all go around the . . . . . .

⑦   **Read and follow the instructions.**

1   VOBITALLZOO
2   GOODTAKEDOG
3   BABYERABALL
4   SIFROMUSICE
5   ACATCHATTER
6   FUBOXEGGINS
7   ESHAZAMFOUR

1. Find the name of an animal with four legs and draw a line through this word.

    Find the opposite of *give* and draw a line through this word.

    Draw a circle around the first four letters.

2. Find something you use in tennis and cricket and draw a line through this word.

    Draw a circle around the opposite of *Hi!*

3. Draw a line through the first two letters.

    Draw a line through the last five letters.

    Now draw a circle around a word. This word has four letters.

4. Draw a line through the first letter.

    Find the name of an animal and draw a line through this word.

    Draw a circle around the other letters.

5. Find the name of something to eat and draw a line through this word.

    Find the opposite of *out*. Draw a line through this word.

    Find the missing word – On Mars, the Book of Adabra was inside a . . . .

    Draw a circle around this word.

6. You say this word to make a magic spell. Draw a line through this word.

    Find a number word. Draw a circle around this word.

Can you read the message?

Picture dictionary

Complete the words. Then colour the pictures.

a _ _ _ _

a _ _ _ _ _ _ _ _

b _ _ d _ _ _ _ _

c _ _ _

d _ _ _ _ _

f _ _ _ _ _

f _ _ _ _ _ _

h _ _ _ _ _ _ _ _

l _ _ _ _ _

m _ _ _ _ _ _ _

n _ _ _ _

p _ _ _ _ _ _

s _ _ _ _ _ _ _ _

s _ _ _

s _ _ _ _ _ _

v _ _

a _ _ _ _ _ _ _ _

Complete the words. *It's made of . . .*

c _ _ _ _ _   g _ _ _ _   m _ _ _ _   p _ _ _ _

p _ _ _ _ _ _   s _ _ _ _   w _ _ _   w _ _ _

The Solar System

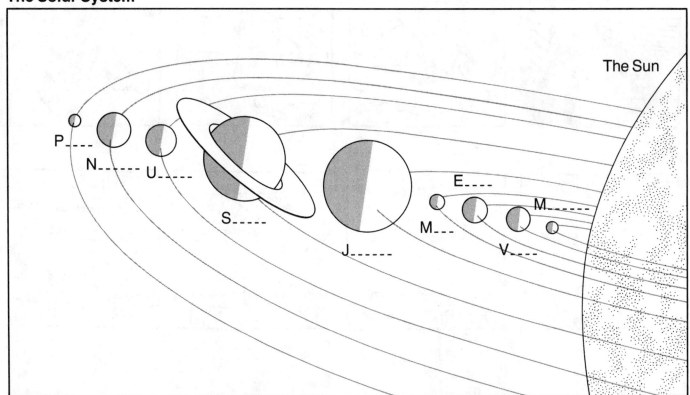

The Sun

P _ _ _ _

N _ _ _ _ _   U _ _ _ _

S _ _ _ _ _

J _ _ _ _ _ _

E _ _ _ _

M _ _ _

M _ _ _ _ _

V _ _ _ _